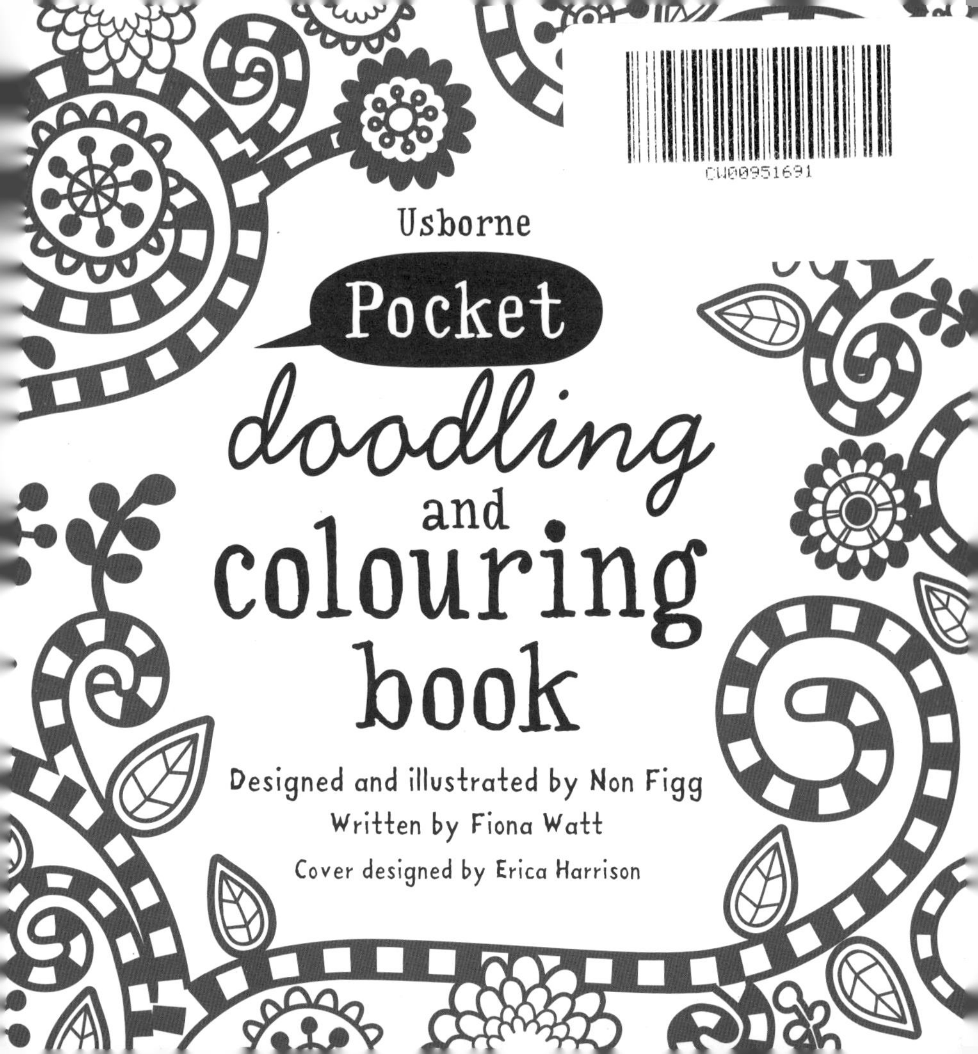
CW00951691
Usborne
Pocket
doodling
and
colouring
book
Designed and illustrated by Non Figg
Written by Fiona Watt
Cover designed by Erica Harrison

Draw eyes, mouths and fins on the sea creatures.

Draw some stars, planets and spaceships.

Draw as many cats as you can. Then, add markings and paw prints.

Doodle flowers. Doodle flowers. Doodle flowers. Doodle flowers.

Draw a creature to go with this long, curly tail.

Maybe it needs patterns or scales...?

Draw more penguins... and more penguins.

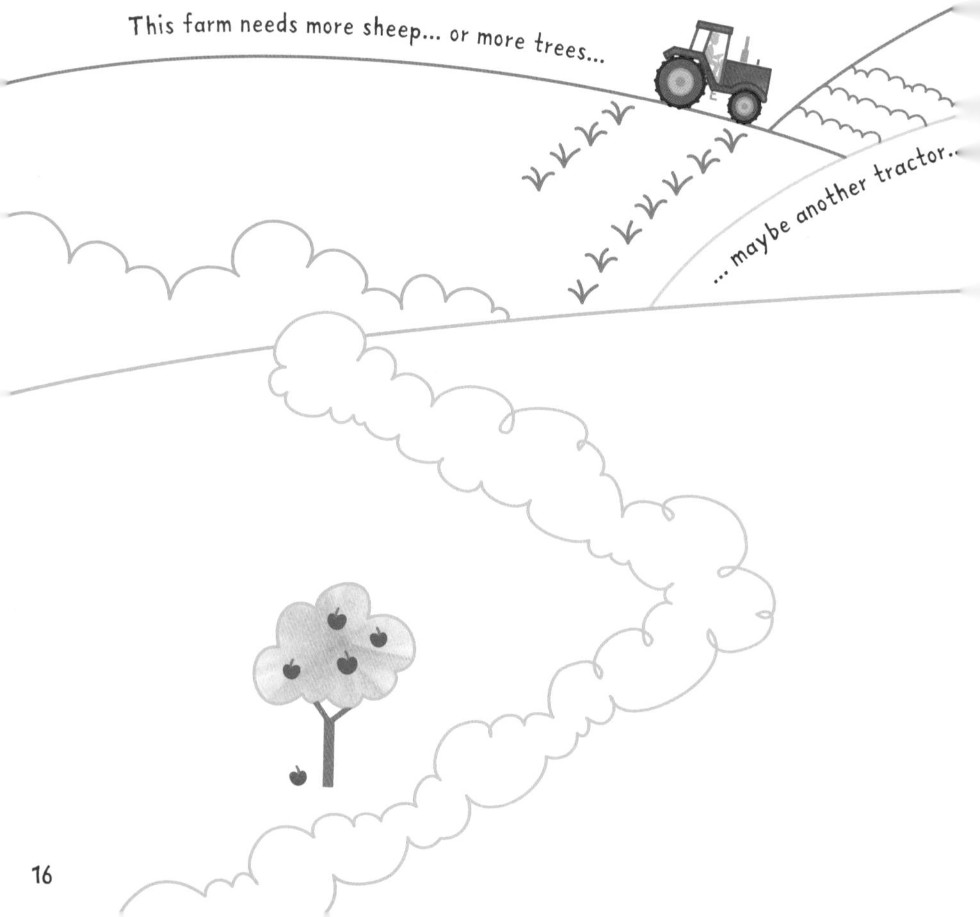

This farm needs more sheep... or more trees...

... maybe another tractor...

... perhaps some cows... or a rabbit?

Turn each squiggle into something.

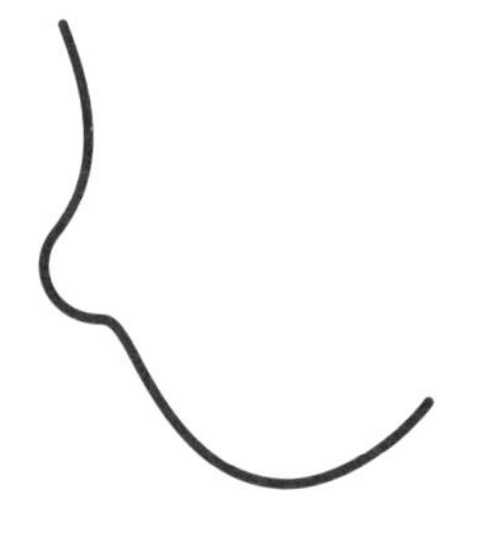

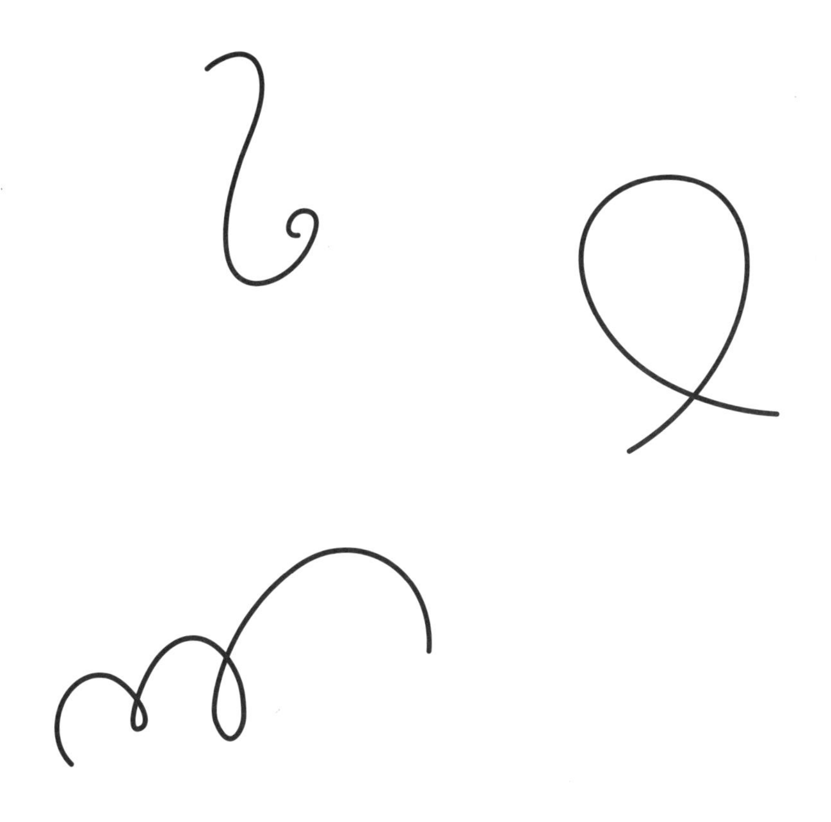

Draw lots of things in the windows.

Doodle hair and faces.

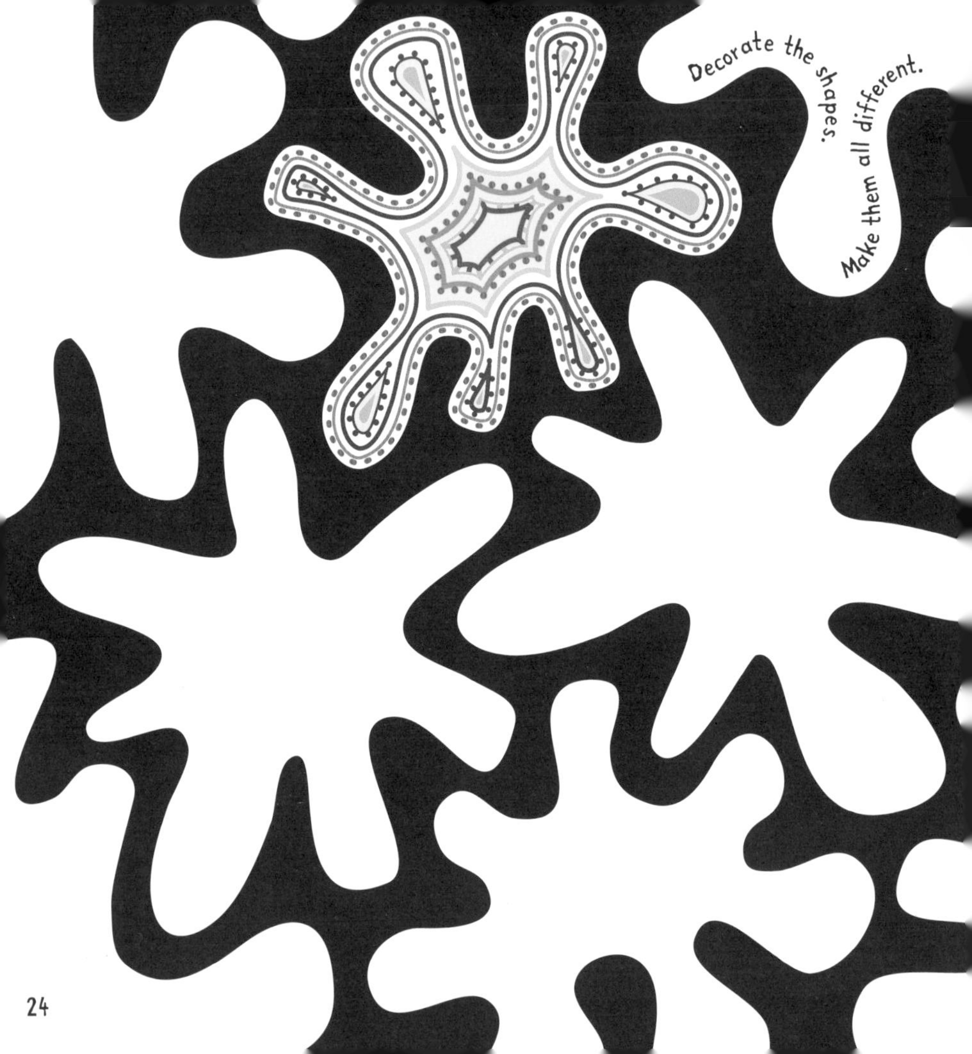
Decorate the shapes.
Make them all different.

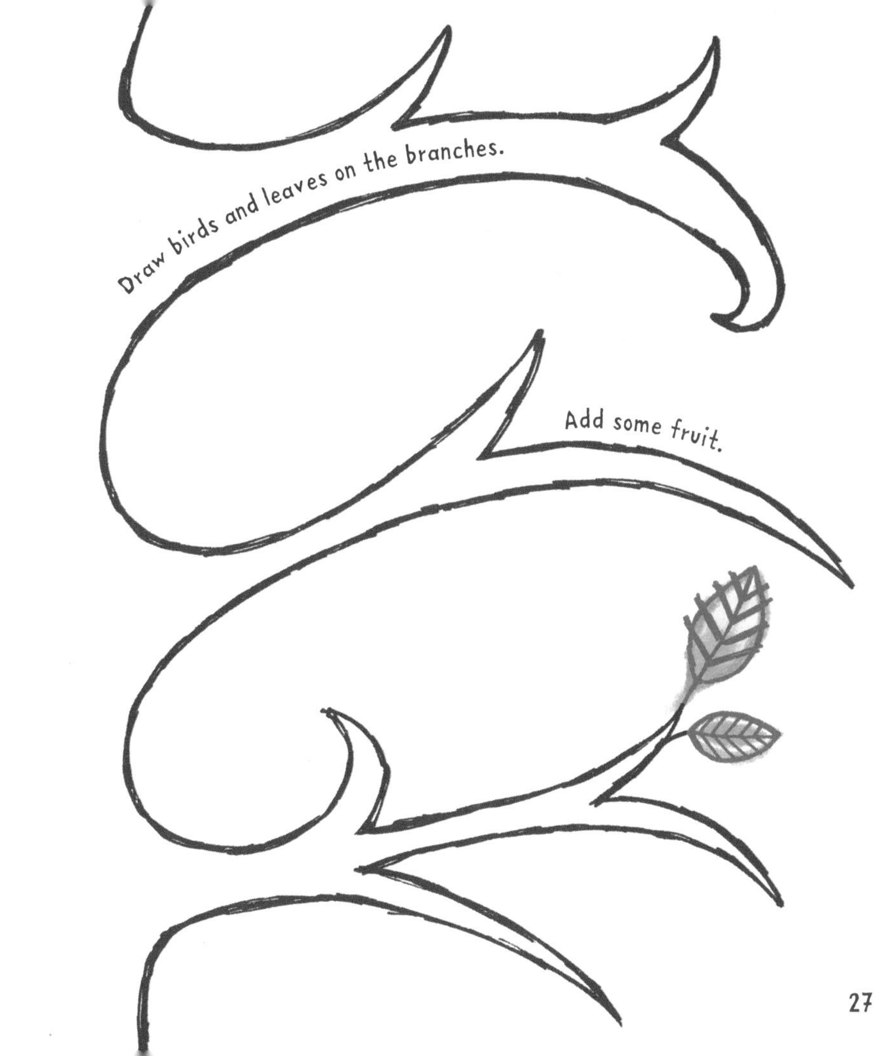
Draw birds and leaves on the branches.
Add some fruit.

Draw along the grid lines to add to the pattern.

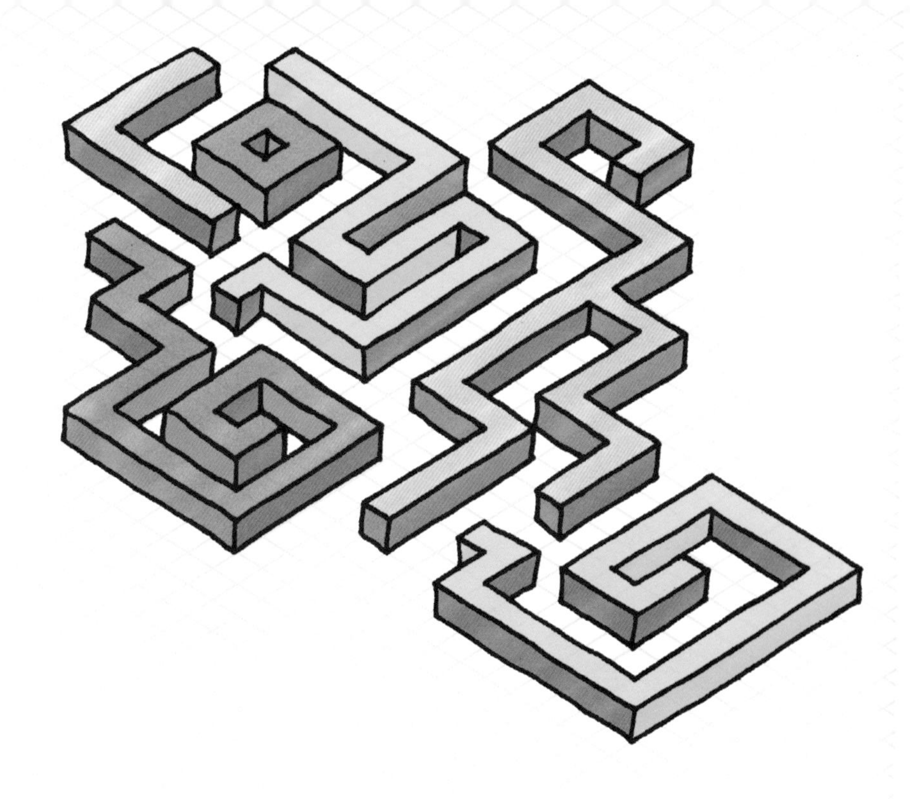

Decorate these slime monsters and doodle some more slithering across the pages.

Doodle food on the plates.

Fill the slopes with skiers having fun in the snow.

Draw some more creepers.
Maybe there's something
hiding among them?

Fill the equipment with bubbling liquids and potions.

Doodle on the shapes to turn them into monsters.

Draw more flowers and doodle on the vases.

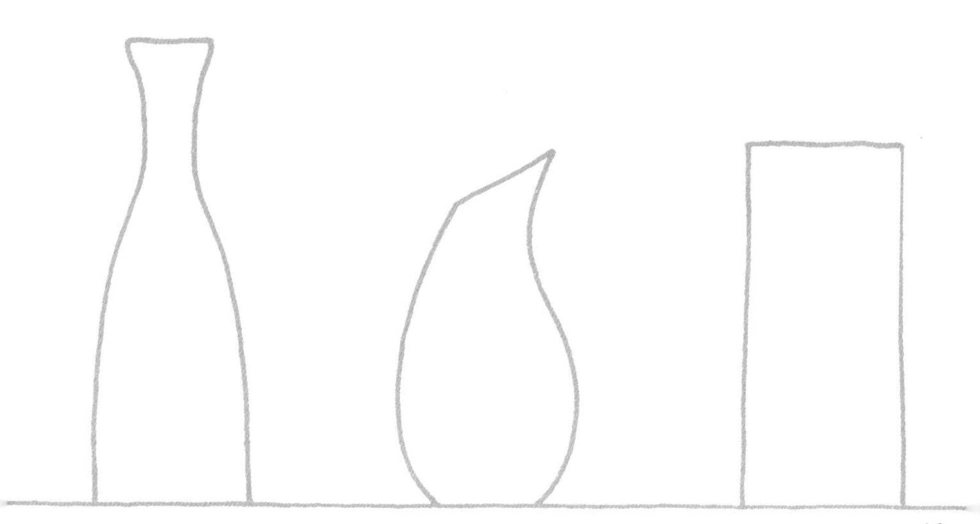

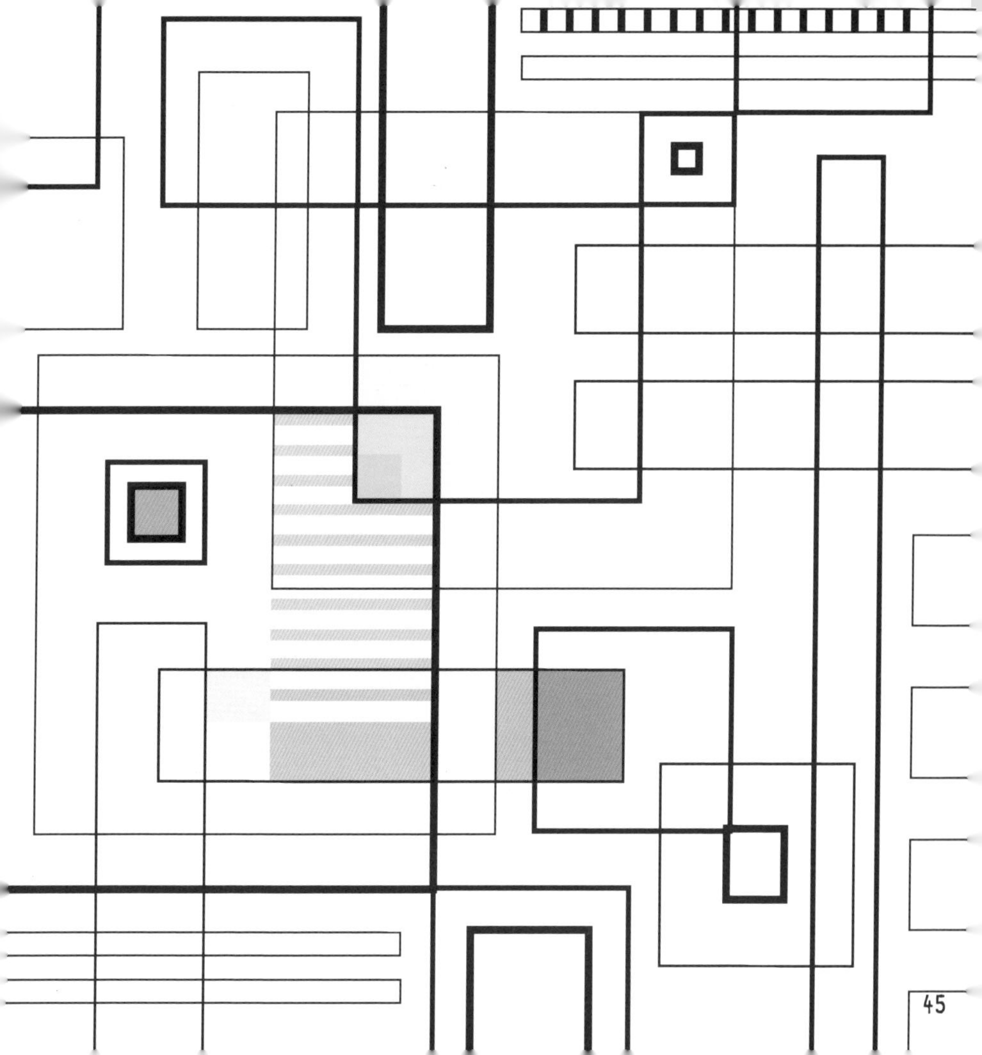

Make patterns...
...or just colour in the circles.

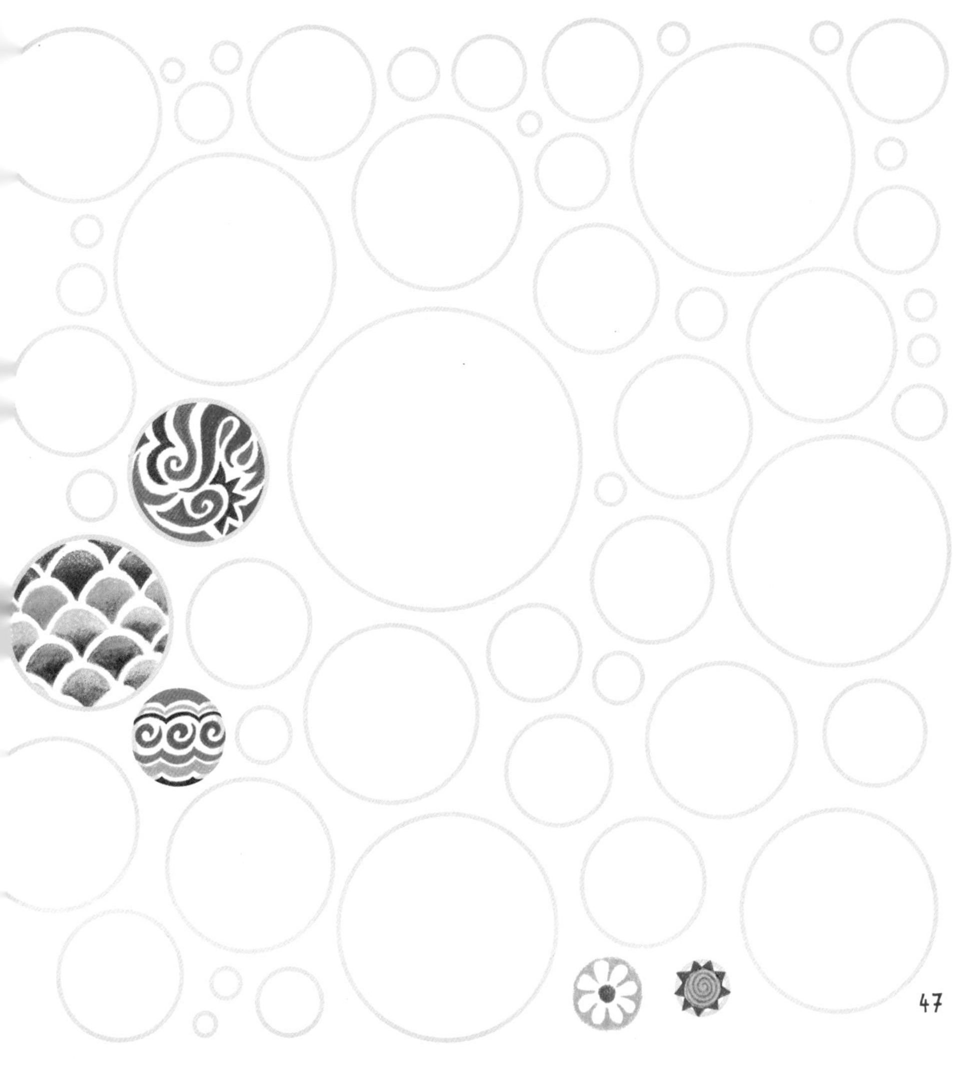

Draw more fish and lilies in the pond.

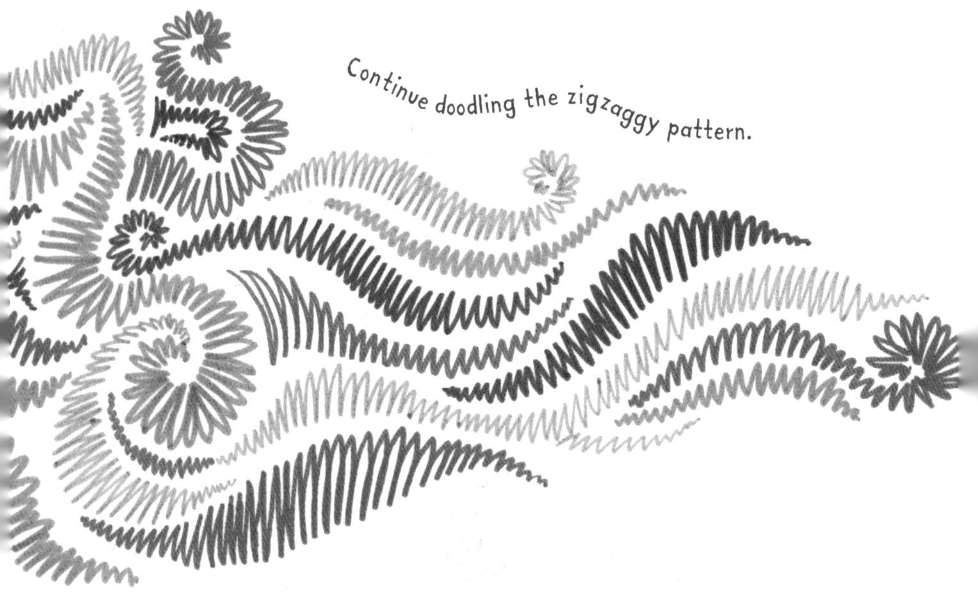
Continue doodling the zigzaggy pattern.

Draw pictures in the frames.

Decorate the racing cars and design some more.

Colour...colour...colour

Turn the shapes into faces.

Fill in the shoes and design some of your own.

Doodle on the shapes to make flying monsters...

... or running monsters...

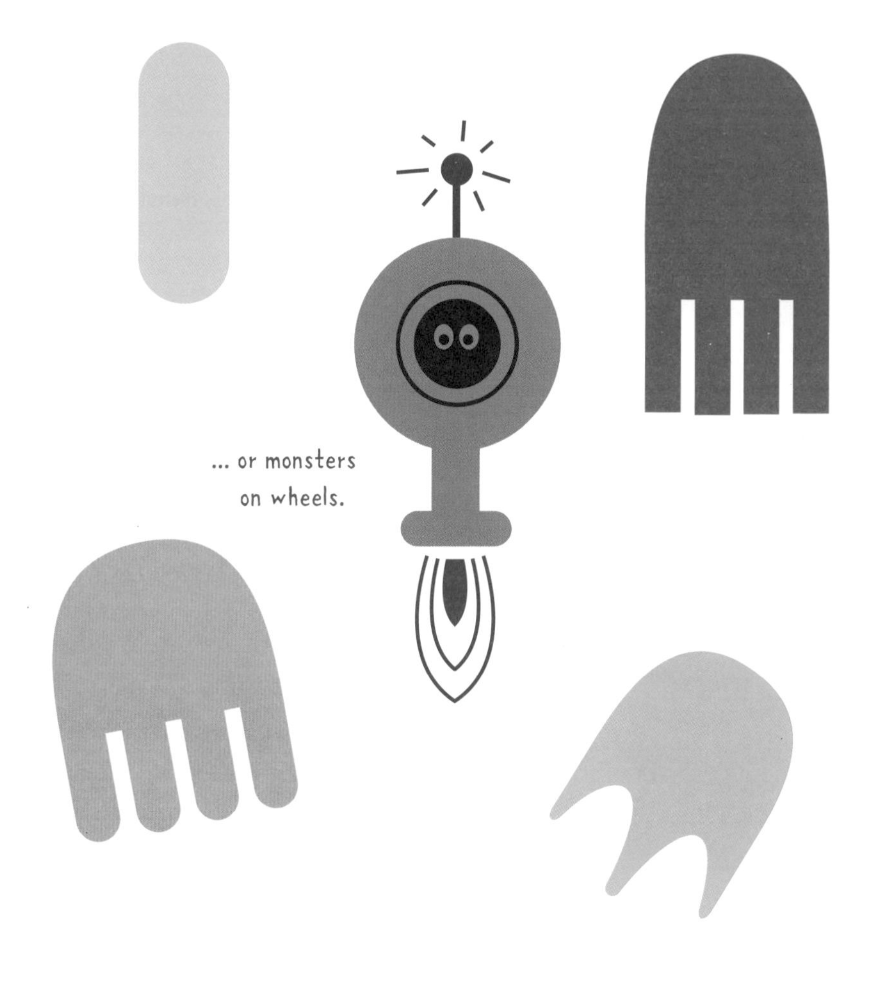

... or monsters
on wheels.

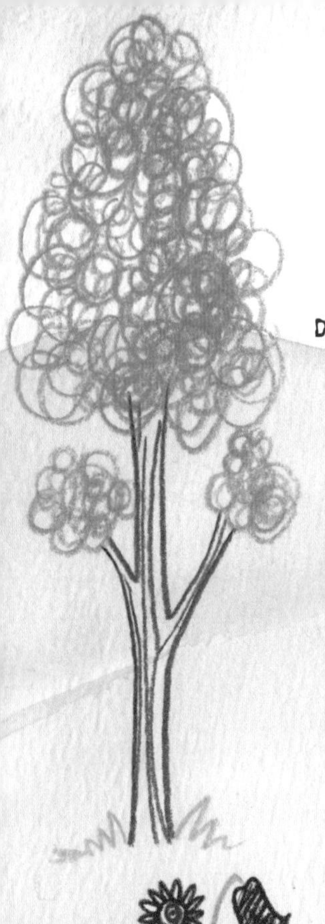

Doodle more trees.

Add some flowers, some birds and maybe some animals?

Design more robots.

Doodle on the shapes to turn them into birds.

Doodle ships and boats on the sea.

Add lots of flowers...

...and some leaves, too.

Doodle what's beneath the city.

Doodle patterns on the snakes.

Doodle more food.

Copy these birds.

Design some of
your own, too.

Doodle bright leaves blowing in the wind.

Doodle a hat on each head.

Draw lots and lots of cat faces.

Fill the shelves with clothes and accessories.

Doodle things in the bottles and jars.

Design a butterfly.

Doodle a moth.

Doodle more scribbly creatures.

Doodle some birds flying in the sky and add a few clouds.

Keep on doodling without taking your pen off the paper.

Fill these pages with stars.

Draw birds in the cages, then draw over all the lines on the cages.

Draw more sharks and more fish...

... and perhaps
some sea horses too.

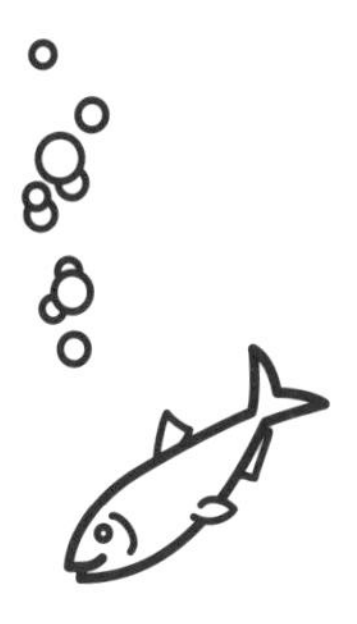

Doodle more doodles.

Draw more bats
flying across
the sky.

Doodle fish, weeds, coral and pebbles, and anything else you can think of that lives under the sea.

Transform these shapes into monsters, then doodle some more.

Fill in the doodle.

Add shapes to the pattern and make it grow bigger and bigger.

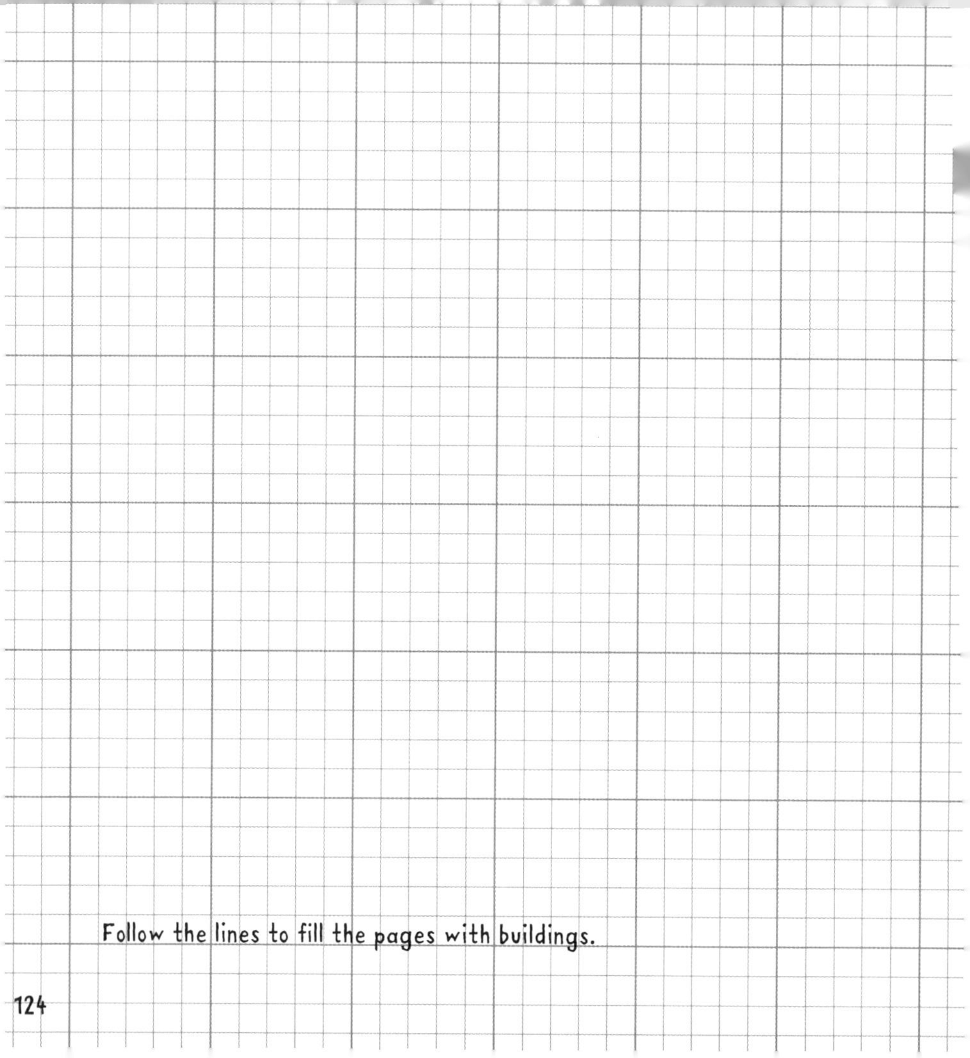

Follow the lines to fill the pages with buildings.

Draw what you might see through the magnifying glass.

First published in 2010 by Usborne Publishing Ltd., Usborne House, 83-85 Saffron Hill, London EC1N 8RT, England. www.usborne.com 